Stephen Berg

I Love
Soccer!

Illustrations by
Gary Undercuffler

Sole
BOOKS

Wild Soccer USA, Inc.
P.O. Box 10445
Beverly Hills, CA 90213

Special thanks to:
Yonatan, Yaron, and Guy Ginsberg

Library of Congress cataloging-in–Publication data available.

ISBN 978-1-938591-00-6

Published by Sole Books

First edition July 2012

Printed in China

Layout: Lynn M. Snyder

10987654321

Hi soccer fans!

I played my first soccer game
when I was five years old!

I scored eight goals and
it was so fun!

I love this game very much!

If you already play,
you know how great it feels.

If you don't, it's easy! Just take a ball and kick it around.

Your friend and teammate,

Landon Donovan

Hi.
My name is Logan.
In my family, everyone plays soccer.
Even our dog, Lucky!

The soccer ball is round.
It feels great to kick it.

Our team's name is the Fireballs.
My teammates are very nice.

Both boys and girls can play soccer.
We wear soccer uniforms
and shoes, called cleats.

Each player has a number.
My number is 7.

This is the soccer field.
Each team has to kick the ball
into the other team's goal.

There are eleven players on a soccer team.
On our team, we only have seven players.

A field player moves the ball with his feet.
He can pass, kick, and dribble the ball.

The Goal Keeper has to stop the ball from entering into the goal!

Before the game, our coach tells us
how we should play.

The referee tosses a coin.
We get to choose which side of the field
we want to play.

The game is on.
Our forward kicks the ball as hard as he can!

He scores!   GOAL!!!

The referee makes sure we are playing
according to the rules.
Two assistant referees help the referee.

I'm a midfielder. I have to get the ball
from our defenders and pass it to our forwards.

The other team is on the attack.
Their striker dribbles and shoots!
He misses!

The game is really hard.
I'm tired and I'm covered
in sweat, but it feels good.

The score is a draw, 3 to 3.
One minute left to the end of the game.
I shoot. It goes in! We win!

It is great to win!
We have to respect the other team.
They played very hard.

I can't wait until the next game!
My dad calls it "the beautiful game!"
He is right!

WHAT DO THESE WORDS MEAN?

<u>Soccer ball:</u> It is round and bouncy. It gets round because we pump air into it!

<u>Soccer uniforms:</u> The entire team wears the same uniform: a jersey (shirt), shorts, shin-guards (to protect the shins), socks and cleats.

<u>Referee:</u> The referee makes sure that everyone plays by the rules.

<u>Coach:</u> The coach teaches the players how to play and gives the instructions during the game.

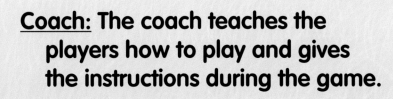

Team: A group of players who play together.

Pass: Kicking the ball to your teammate.

Dribble: Moving the ball with your feet.

Foul: When a player plays against the rules.

Soccer field: Where soccer is played.

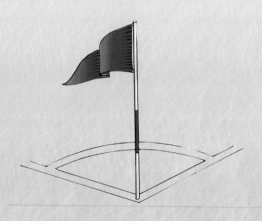

FUN QUIZ

A. Who wins a soccer game?
B. Who can touch the ball with his/her hands?
C. What is the name of soccer shoes?
D. What is a draw?